Contents

Grade 2

ISBN: 978-1-927042-05-2

The Bumblebee

The bumblebee is an insect. It is yellow and black and has six legs. Most bumblebees live in a group in a nest. Each group or colony has a queen, worker bees, and drones. The queen is the leader.

The queen bee lays four to eight eggs in the nest after a winter in hibernation. These eggs hatch to become worker bees and drones. The colony grows until it has 50 to 600 bees. The worker bees help new plants grow and they make honey from the nectar in flowering plants.

A. Read the story and answer the questions.

1. What kind of animal is a bumblebee?

   _____

2. What colour is a bumblebee?

   _____

3. Who is the leader of the bumblebee colony?

   _____

4. When does the queen bee lay eggs?

   _____

ISBN: 978-1-927042-05-2

Phonics: Beginning Consonants

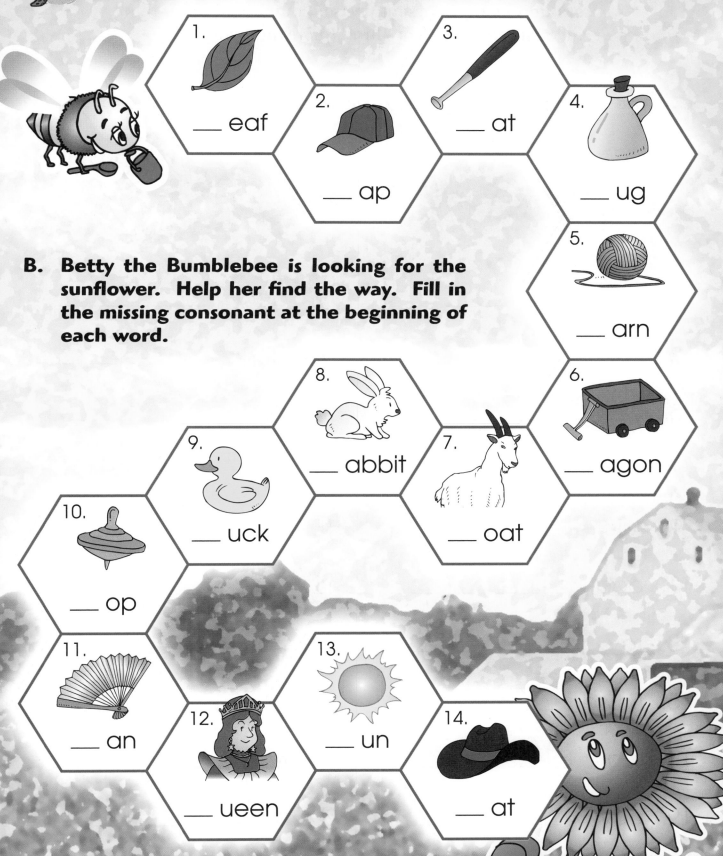

B. Betty the Bumblebee is looking for the sunflower. Help her find the way. Fill in the missing consonant at the beginning of each word.

1. ___ eaf

2. ___ ap

3. ___ at

4. ___ ug

5. ___ arn

6. ___ agon

7. ___ oat

8. ___ abbit

9. ___ uck

10. ___ op

11. ___ an

12. ___ ueen

13. ___ un

14. ___ at

ISBN: 978-1-927042-05-2

 Common Nouns

- A **common noun** names any person, animal, place, or thing.
- It can be singular (one) or plural (more than one).

C. Add "s" to write the plural form of the singular nouns.

1. bee _____

2. dog _____

3. insect _____

4. desk _____

5. ship _____

6. table _____

7. bear _____

8. girl _____

9. ruler _____

10. lake _____

11. boat _____

12. road _____

13. toy _____

14. tree _____

15. flower _____

16. plant _____

17. rug _____

18. flag _____

19. boy _____

20. mask _____

ISBN: 978-1-927042-05-2

Code Word Game

D. Use the code below to read the sentences.

A	B	C	D	E	F	G	H	I	J	K	L	M	N	O
1	2	3	4	5	6	7	8	9	10	11	12	13	14	15

P	Q	R	S	T	U	V	W	X	Y	Z
16	17	18	19	20	21	22	23	24	25	26

1.
```
__  __ __ __ __ __ __
1   19 17 21 1  18 5

__ __  __  __ __ __ __ __
9  19  1   19 8  1  16 5

__ __ __ __   __ __ __ __
23 9  20 8    6  15 21 18

__ __ __ __ __
5  17 21 1  12

__ __ __ __ __ .
19 9  4  5  19
```

2.
```
__   __ __ __ __ __ __ __ __
1    20 18 9  1  14 7  12 5

__ __  __  __ __ __ __ __
9  19  1   19 8  1  16 5

__ __ __ __   __ __ __ __ __
23 9  20 8    20 8  18 5  5

__ __ __ __ __ .
19 9  4  5  19
```

3.
```
__  __ __ __ __ __ __
1   3  9  18 3  12 5

__ __  __  __ __ __ __ __ __
9  19  1   19 9  14 7  12 5

__ __ __ __ .
12 9  14 5
```

4.
```
__  __ __ __ __ __ __ __ __ __
1   18 5  3  20 1  14 7  12 5

__ __  __  __ __ __ __ __
9  19  1   19 8  1  16 5

__ __ __ __
23 9  20 8

__ __ __ __ __ __ __ __
15 16 16 15 19 9  20 5

__ __ __ __ __   __ __ __ __
19 9  4  5  19   20 8  1  20

__ __ __   __ __ __ __ __ __ .
1  18 5    5  17 21 1  12
```

ISBN: 978-1-927042-05-2

The Museum Trip

Tomorrow our class is going on a trip to the ROM (Royal Ontario Museum). We will leave school at 9:00 a.m. and return at 3:00 p.m. We will have to take our lunch with us.

When we get to the museum, we will visit the Bat Cave, the dinosaurs, and the Egyptian mummies.

The day after our trip, when we get back to school, we will draw pictures and write about what we saw there.

ROM
Royal Ontario Museum

A. Read the story and circle the correct answers.

1. What is the story about?

   A. visiting the school   B. a trip to the museum
   C. looking at dinosaurs

2. What will the children take with them?

   A. snacks   B. lunch   C. a school bag

3. Which of these will they see?

   A. paintings   B. mummies   C. toys

4. What will they do after the trip?

   A. play a game   B. watch a movie   C. draw pictures

ISBN: 978-1-927042-05-2

Phonics: **Middle and Ending Consonants**

B. **Look at the pictures. Fill in the missing consonants.**

1  bu ___

2 bo ___

3 nes ___

4  di ___ e

5  tuli ___

6  mas ___

7 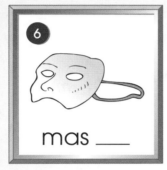 ba ___

8 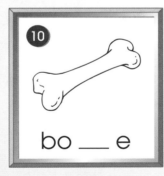 po ___

9 pe ___

10  bo ___ e

11  ca ___

12  bal ___

13  soc ___

14  sa ___

15 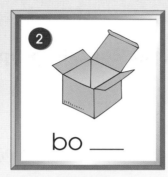 ki ___ e

16 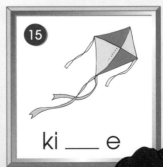 ra ___ e

ISBN: 978-1-927042-05-2

Unit 2

Proper Nouns

- A **proper noun** names a specific person, animal, place, or thing.
- It always begins with a capital letter.

C. Colour the pages of the books that contain proper nouns.

1. museum | ROM
2. Ontario | province
3. Venus | planet
4. Mrs. Smith | mother
5. boy | Mark
6. dog | Punkie
7. Portland Drive | street
8. Mars | chocolate bar
9. Canada Day | holiday
10. day | Sunday
11. Ottawa | city
12. Charlotte's Web | book
13. Deer Lake | town
14. month | May

ISBN: 978-1-927042-05-2

Alike and Different

- You can compare things by looking at how they are alike and how they are different. If two things are **alike**, something about them is the same. If two things are **different**, something about them is not the same.

D. Read each sentence. Put a check mark ✔ in the box to indicate the sport being described.

	Hockey	Baseball
1. We play it on ice.		
2. We play it on a field.		
3. Something is hit.		
4. There are goalposts.		
5. Players run.		
6. Players wear skates.		
7. Players wear caps.		
8. Scores are kept.		

ISBN: 978-1-927042-05-2

The Channel Tunnel

Have you heard of the Channel Tunnel? It is an undersea tunnel. We can travel from England to France through this tunnel.

The idea of a tunnel running under the English Channel is not new. As early as 1802, a French engineer tried to convince the emperor Napoleon to build one. In 1993, it was finally built.

The Channel Tunnel actually consists of three tunnels: one for trains that carry people in one direction and another for trains to carry people in the opposite direction. A third service tunnel allows fresh air, repair workers, and emergency vehicles to reach the train tunnels.

A. Read the story and answer the questions.

1. Which countries does the Channel Tunnel link?

_____

2. When was the Channel Tunnel built?

_____

ISBN: 978-1-927042-05-2

3. Who was the French emperor in 1802?

_____

4. What are the three tunnels for?

_____

Phonics: Short Vowels

B. Rob is looking for the tunnel. Help him find his way. Fill in the missing vowels a, e, i, o, or u.

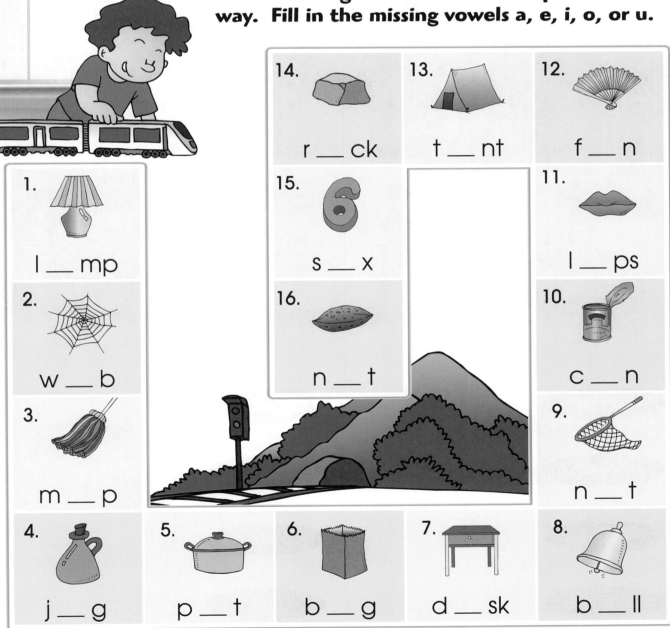

14. r __ ck

13. t __ nt

12. f __ n

15. s __ x

11. l __ ps

16. n __ t

10. c __ n

9. n __ t

1. l __ mp

2. w __ b

3. m __ p

4. j __ g

5. p __ t

6. b __ g

7. d __ sk

8. b __ ll

ISBN: 978-1-927042-05-2

Plural Nouns

C. Look at the picture. Find the objects listed below. Count them and write the number words with the plural nouns.

street light		car	

flower		boy	

bicycle		tree	

parking meter		truck	

ISBN: 978-1-927042-05-2

Classification / Grouping

D. Louise the Ladybug wants to sort some words.
Write the words that belong to each group
under the first word.

cup   blackboard   desk   swing   eraser

seesaw   pear   bowl   slide   tires   horn

grapes   apple   glass   key

1. cupboard

_____

_____

_____

2. school

_____

_____

3. car

_____

_____

4. playground

_____

_____

_____

5. fruit

_____

_____

ISBN: 978-1-927042-05-2

Snakes

A. Jake the Snake needs help to finish the story. Fill in the missing words for him.

Snakes are 1._____ that have 2._____, slender bodies. They have no limbs. They are 3._____-blooded because they have a low body temperature.

Snakes are non-mammals because they lay 4._____ , which hatch soon after they are 5._____ . They go into 6._____ , or a kind of sleep, for part of the year. Snakes shed their 7._____ several times a year. They 8._____ by slithering from one 9._____ to another.

cold   laid   long
eggs   reptiles
hibernation   move
skins   place

ISBN: 978-1-927042-05-2

Phonics: Long Vowels

B. Help Jake the Snake look for his friend. Fill in the blanks with a, i, o, or u.

1

b __ ke

2

h __ ve

3
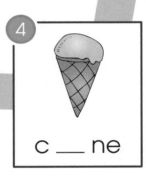
p __ le

6

t __ be

5

c __ ke

4
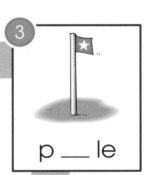
c __ ne

7
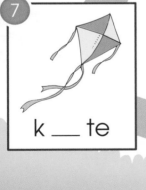
k __ te

8

r __ ler

9

g __ te

10

t __ lip

ISBN: 978-1-927042-05-2

Unit 4

Verbs (Action Words)

- **Verbs** are words that describe actions.
  Example: running – She is running a race.

C. **Find these actions in the picture and write a sentence using each one.**

| swinging | playing | running | climbing | sliding |

1. _____

2. _____

3. _____

4. _____

5. _____

ISBN: 978-1-927042-05-2

Context Clues

D. Fill in the blanks with the words in bold in the story.

Cooking with Mom

Mom and I took out the **recipe** for Rice Krispie Cookies from the recipe **box**. The **ingredients** included Rice Krispies, marshmallows, and butter. We got the Rice Krispies and marshmallows from the **cupboard** and the butter from the **refrigerator**.

We heated the butter in a **pot** on the **stove**. When the butter was **melted**, we added the marshmallows. Then we stirred in the Rice Krispies. Lastly, we scooped the mixture out of the bowl and into a **square** pan.

1. A _____ gives directions for cooking.

2. My brother keeps his toys in a _____ .

3. The _____ are the things used in cooking something.

4. We often keep dry ingredients in a _____ .

5. I store butter in a _____ .

6. You can heat chocolate chunks in a _____

    on a _____ until it is _____ .

7. Our cookie mixture went into a _____ pan.

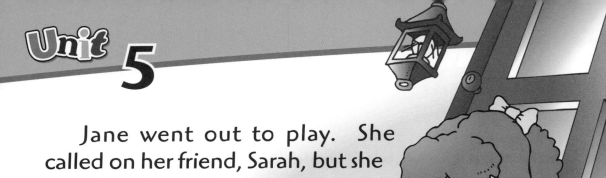

Jane went out to play. She called on her friend, Sarah, but she wasn't at home. Then she went to Christine's house, but she wasn't at home either. Jane felt sad. There was no one to play with.

A. Write what you think will happen next. Give the story to a friend and ask him/her to write his/her ideas beside yours.

Your Ideas	Your Friend's Ideas

ISBN: 978-1-927042-05-2

Phonics: Vowel Digraphs – ai and ay

B. Find the words with "ai" and "ay" that match the riddles.

play	day	jay	paint	tray	tail
snail	say	pay	nail		

1. I carry my house on my back.

   _____

2. I have 24 hours.

   _____

3. I hold things together when you are building.

   _____

4. I am a blue bird.

   _____

5. You can carry things on me.

   _____

6. I make colourful pictures.

   _____

7. I am found at the back of a dog.

   _____

8. You must do this if you want to buy something.

   _____

9. This is what you do when you speak.

   _____

10. You like to do this with your friends.

   _____

ISBN: 978-1-927042-05-2

Unit 5

"Being" Verbs (am, is, are)

- *"Am"*, *"is"*, and *"are"* are special verbs that tell about someone or something.

  Rules: Use "am" with "I".

  Use "is" when it is one person, animal, place, or thing.

  Use "are" when it is more than one person, animal, place, or thing.

C. Fill in the blanks with "am", "is", or "are".

1. Jane _____ waiting for her friend.

2. Kathleen and David _____ flying a kite.

3. She _____ planning to see the circus.

4. Maria _____ running to the bus.

5. There _____ three boys in the play.

6. They _____ best friends.

7. We _____ looking for the soccer ball.

8. I _____ going to the show with my dad.

9. Jason _____ riding his bike.

10. It _____ a nice morning.

ISBN: 978-1-927042-05-2

Word Search

D. Find the words below in the word search.

snail   may   tray   nail   trail   day
clay   say   hail   play   sail   pray

q	w	f	s	w	h	o	f	x	f	h	k	t
h	b	k	n	e	b	k	r	b	h	l	g	r
r	o	x	a	l	m	n	o	k	l	w	z	a
p	k	f	i	q	a	g	z	l	z	s	n	i
q	g	c	l	a	y	o	c	z	n	a	i	l
r	o	e	q	c	d	k	d	r	f	y	j	h
b	h	q	t	e	l	f	e	s	w	e	h	f
q	x	o	r	v	b	p	r	a	y	r	l	n
z	d	r	a	f	w	f	w	d	n	p	q	l
p	l	a	y	w	o	x	o	r	s	t	i	s
s	t	x	x	h	e	d	x	h	x	a	x	h
g	d	h	b	o	l	k	b	c	h	r	i	m
r	a	o	f	r	b	s	l	e	t	s	g	l
h	y	m	l	x	m	l	b	x	n	a	y	b

ISBN: 978-1-927042-05-2

A. Ben the Bunny has a special week ahead. Can you guess what will happen on each day? Finish the sentences.

1. On Sunday, it will be Easter.

2. On Monday, Ben _____

3. On Tuesday, _____

4. On Wednesday, _____

5. On Thursday, _____

6. On Friday, _____

ISBN: 978-1-927042-05-2

7. Draw a picture of something you think Ben would like to do on Saturday and complete the sentence.

On Saturday, _____

_____

_____

_____

_____

Saturday

Phonics: Vowel Digraphs – ea and ee

B. Circle the correct word to complete each sentence.

1. There are seven days in a weak   week .

2. The blue jeans   beans are hanging on the line.

3. It is nice to have a cup of tea   tee .

4. The baseball teem   team plays in summer.

5. The bean   been plant grew very high.

6. We will have some meat   meet for dinner.

7. Mom is going to weed   week the garden.

8. The bee   beat makes its home in a hive.

9. We sail our boat on the sea   see .

10. This seed   seek will grow into a plant.

ISBN: 978-1-927042-05-2

Unit 6

Past Tense Verbs

- Some **verbs** tell what happened in the past. You can add "**ed**" to them.

C. Add "ed" to the clue words and complete the crossword puzzle.

Across

A. plant
B. want
C. train
D. end
E. learn

Down

1. treat
2. sail
3. play
4. answer
5. need

ISBN: 978-1-927042-05-2

Unscrambling Words

D. **Unscramble the words and write them in the correct order on the lines.**

P

ptmeSereb	yaM	udseTay	raaJuny	yJlu
cmbeDeer	ydaFir	suAutg	eJnu	sneWdeyda
cObreto	nSdyua	yeFbuarr	odyaMn	crhaM
shTuyard	vmNeorbe	udraStya	lArpi	

Months of the Year

_____

_____

_____

_____

_____

_____

_____

_____

_____

_____

_____

_____

The days of the week and months of the year begin with a capital letter.

Days of the Week

_____

_____

_____

_____

_____

_____

_____

ISBN: 978-1-927042-05-2

The CN (Canadian National) Tower in Toronto, Canada was built in 1976. It is one of the tallest self-supporting towers in the world. It is as high as five and a half football fields and has a foundation that is as deep as a five-storey building.

The CN Tower was built to improve the broadcasting of radio and television signals. Many people have used it to break world records, like the person who hopped down its 1899 steps on a pogo stick.

The CN Tower

A. Read the story and finish the sentences.

1. The CN Tower is one of the tallest _____
   _____

2. It is as high as _____

3. Its foundation is _____

4. The CN Tower was built to _____
   _____

5. One of the world records at the CN Tower was _____
   _____
   _____

ISBN: 978-1-927042-05-2

Phonics: Consonant Blends – bl, cl, fl, gl, pl, and sl

B. **Fill in the blanks with the correct consonant blends.**

| bl | cl | fl | gl | pl | sl |

1. We have a _____ear view of the CN Tower from here.

2. Michael saw the _____owns at the circus.

3. The children played on the _____ide.

4. His new car is _____ack.

5. The _____ass broke into many pieces.

6. They took the _____ed out in the winter.

7. There is a Canadian _____ag in front of our school.

8. Clare _____ew out the candles on the cake.

9. Maggie put the cookies on the _____ate.

10. They were _____ad they took their time.

11. The _____ock in the hall struck midnight.

12. At recess, we _____ay outside.

ISBN: 978-1-927042-05-2

Irregular Past Tense Verbs

- Some **past tense verbs** do not end in "ed".
  Examples: sing ➡ sang; speak ➡ spoke

C. Match the present and past tenses.

1. build •   • thought
2. drink •   • built
3. ring •   • drank
4. think •   • left
5. drive •   • drove
6. leave •   • rang

D. Write the present form of the past tense verbs in the cakes.

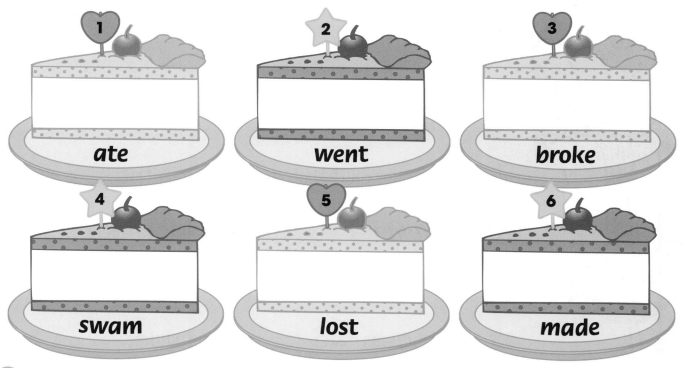

1. ate
2. went
3. broke
4. swam
5. lost
6. made

ISBN: 978-1-927042-05-2

Identifying Polygons

A polygon is a shape with three or more sides.

E. **Draw the shape that matches each description. Label it.**

1. a polygon with three sides

2. a polygon with four sides

3. a polygon with six sides

4. a polygon with seven sides

5. a polygon with five sides

6. a polygon with eight sides

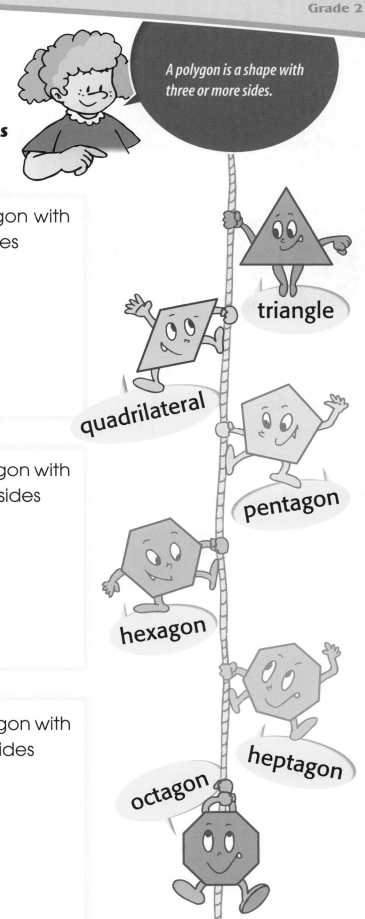

triangle

quadrilateral

pentagon

hexagon

heptagon

octagon

ISBN: 978-1-927042-05-2

Sir John A. Macdonald

The first prime minister of Canada was Sir John A. Macdonald. He was born in Glasgow, Scotland in 1815 and came to Kingston, Ontario in 1820 at the age of five. He became a lawyer in 1836.

In 1867, the Dominion of Canada was formed with Sir John A. Macdonald as its leading figure. He was best known for his part in the completion of the Pacific Railway. He died in 1891 in Ottawa, the nation's capital.

A. Read the story and answer the questions.

1. Who was the first prime minister of Canada?

   _____

2. Where was he born?

   _____

3. How old was he when he came to Ontario?

   _____

4. When was the Dominion of Canada formed?

   _____

5. What was Sir John A. Macdonald best known for?

   _____

ISBN: 978-1-927042-05-2

Phonics: Consonant Blends – br, cr, dr, fr, gr, pr, and tr

B. Fill in the blanks with the consonant blends on the bricks below.

br   cr   dr   fr   gr   pr   tr

_____ une	_____ ime	_____ op
_____ oom	_____ ape	_____ ing
_____ eam	_____ uit	_____ aid
_____ ass	_____ one	_____ ize
_____ ap	_____ ee	_____ og
_____ um	_____ ess	_____ uck
_____ ab	_____ ail	_____ ue
_____ ip	_____ eed	_____ ame
_____ een	_____ ime	_____ oss
_____ ee	_____ ail	_____ oom

ISBN: 978-1-927042-05-2

 Adjectives

- An **adjective** is a word that describes a person, an animal, a place, or a thing.
  Example: The <u>little</u> girl is wearing a <u>new</u> dress.

C. Underline the two adjectives in each sentence.

1. The tired boys rested under the shady tree.

2. He put a big book into a small bag.

3. The friendly nurse is helping the sick girl.

4. The old man is talking to the young child.

5. She picked a red apple from the tall tree.

6. The prime minister was a great man.

D. Use each pair of adjectives to make a sentence.

1. small and round
2. soft and fluffy
3. bright and colourful
4. long and thin

1. _____

2. _____

3. _____

4. _____

ISBN: 978-1-927042-05-2

Ordinal Numbers

- **Ordinal numbers** are words that state the order of people or things.

E. Look at the pictures and their ordinal numbers. Complete the sentences below.

first

second

third

fourth

fifth

sixth

seventh

eighth

ninth

tenth

1. The football is the _____ .

2. The golf ball is the _____ .

3. The baseball is the _____ .

4. The volleyball is the _____ .

5. The tennis ball is the _____ .

6. The basketball is the _____ .

7. The beach ball is the _____ .

8. The shuttlecock is the _____ .

9. The hockey puck is the _____ .

10. The ping-pong ball is the _____ .

ISBN: 978-1-927042-05-2

dance ten
hip-hop fun
good day
many
slippers ballet
costumes

A. Fill in the blanks to complete the story.

When Kathleen was three years old, she started to learn 1._____ . She wore a pink leotard and tiny ballet 2._____ . She practised the steps every 3._____ .

By the time she was 4._____ years old, she was very good at ballet. She learned 5._____ new steps and routines. In no time at all, she was very 6._____ at jazz, too!

Later, when Kathleen was 18, she saw a 7._____ competition on television. She liked the dancers and the 8._____ , too. The dancers were the same age as she and they were having 9._____ . Now, Kathleen is learning 10._____ .

ISBN: 978-1-927042-05-2

Phonics: Consonant Blends – sk, sm, sn, sp, st, and sw

B. Circle the correct consonant blends.

1. She st sm arted learning ballet at a very young age.

2. There are many galaxies in outer sk sp ace.

3. There are two sets of sw st airs in our house.

4. Mom cooked dinner on the st sn ove.

5. Oh, no! There's a st sk unk by the tree.

6. The sm sn ake slithered in the grass.

7. What is your sm sn ack for recess?

8. We will go for a sw sp im.

9. She can sp sk ip with a rope.

10. The sm st all child was shy.

11. Kathleen tried to sk sw at the fly.

12. She tried to sp sn ip the thread with the scissors.

13. Can you sm sn ap your fingers?

14. I set the table with a fork, a knife, and a sp sm oon.

ISBN: 978-1-927042-05-2

Sentence Recognition

- A **sentence** is a group of words that tells a complete thought about someone or something.

C. **Underline the groups of words that are not complete sentences.**

1. Polar bears live in the Arctic. They are big and white. Big paws. They have small eyes and ears. Jump from ice floe to ice floe.

2. Polar bears have other names. Sometimes called white bears, sea bears, or ice bears. Swim very well.

3. Polar bears move fast and travel far. Eat seals and fish. The male is usually larger than the female. Hairy feet.

4. Baby bears or cubs are born in winter. Weigh less than one kilogram when born. Remain with mothers from ten months to two years.

ISBN: 978-1-927042-05-2

Riddles

D. Help Sunny solve the riddles below.

Toonies, Loonies, and Such

| penny | nickel | dime | quarter | loonie | toonie |

1. I am worth 1¢.
    I am smaller than a nickel
    but bigger than a dime.
    I have maple leaves.

    _____

2. I am worth $2.00.
    I am silver and gold.
    I am the largest coin.

    _____

3. I am worth 10¢.
    I am the smallest coin.
    I have a schooner called
    the Bluenose.

    _____

4. I am worth 25¢.
    I am larger than a nickel but
    smaller than a loonie.
    I have a caribou.

    _____

5. I am worth $1.00.
    I am golden.
    I have a loon on the front.

    _____

6. I am worth 5¢.
    I am silver.
    I am larger than a dime but
    smaller than a quarter.

    _____

ISBN: 978-1-927042-05-2

Unit 10

The Treasure Chest

Dear Dave,

We went to Sharaz last Thursday. When we arrived, we heard about a sunken ship in the shallow sea. The story goes like this – a pirate ship sank there long ago and there are still treasure chests aboard.

We decided to search for the sunken treasure. First, we boarded a small boat and rowed out to the ship. Then, we put on wetsuits and masks and dived under the water.

When we reached the ship, we swam inside and, guess what? We found a giant chest filled with gold and jewels!

I'll send you some photos as soon as I have them.

Your friend,
Rob

A. Read the letter and answer the questions.

1. What is the main idea of the first paragraph?

_____

_____

2. What is the main idea of the second paragraph?

_____

_____

ISBN: 978-1-927042-05-2

Phonics: Consonant Digraphs – ch, sh, th, and wh

B. **Fill in the missing letters to complete the tongue twisters.**

> Tongue twisters with ch, sh, th, and wh are sometimes hard to say.

ch 1. _____ester _____ewed the _____ewing gum _____eerily.

sh 2. _____e sells sea_____ells by the sea_____ore.

th 3. _____addeus _____ought _____e _____imble was _____ick.

wh 4. Willy the _____ale _____irled _____ile the _____eel of the _____ite _____aler _____istled.

C. **Fill in the blanks with the correct words.**

1. The _____ sank in the sea. (ship, shop)

2. The treasure _____ was filled with jewels. (cheat, chest)

3. A cat's _____ help it find its way. (whisper, whiskers)

4. This gravy is _____ . (thick, think)

5. The _____ is a delicious fruit. (beach, peach)

6. A _____ flies toward light. (moth, math)

ISBN: 978-1-927042-05-2

Unit 10

Subject of a Sentence

- The **subject** part of a sentence tells who or what the sentence is about.

D. Look at the pictures. Write a subject for each sentence.

1. _____ is filled with treasure.

2. _____ are my favourite fruit.

3. _____ orbits the sun.

4. _____ has a monitor and a keyboard.

5. _____ is my favourite sport.

6. _____ is 8:15 a.m.

7. Draw and write.

_____ is what I like to do with my friends.

ISBN: 978-1-927042-05-2

Baby Animals

E. Read the sentences. Look at the pictures and fill in the blanks.

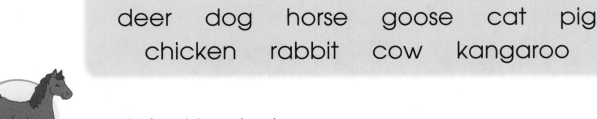

deer   dog   horse   goose   cat   pig
chicken   rabbit   cow   kangaroo

1. A foal is a baby _____ .

2. A calf is a baby _____ .

3. A leveret is a baby _____ .

4. A puppy is a baby _____ .

5. A joey is a baby _____ .

6. A piglet is a baby _____ .

7. A chick is a baby _____ .

8. A gosling is a baby _____ .

9. A kitten is a baby _____ .

10. A fawn is a baby _____ .

ISBN: 978-1-927042-05-2

Unit 11

A Visit to the Farm

There are many different kinds of farms. Some are dairy farms and some are cattle farms. There are others that grow vegetables, like potatoes and carrots. In the West, farmers grow wheat.

Our class visited a farm. It was a dairy farm, so the animals were all cows. The farmer showed us how the cows are milked using big machines.

We had lots of fun at the farm.

A. Read the story and answer the questions.

1. What is the main idea of the first paragraph?

    _____

2. What kind of farm did the children visit?

    _____

3. What did the farmer use to milk the cows?

    _____

ISBN: 978-1-927042-05-2

Phonics: R-controlled Vowels

- When the letter "**r**" follows a vowel, it changes the sound of the vowel.

B. Arnie the Farmer is going to the market. Help him get there. Underline the correct words.

Arnie's (form, farm) is (for, far) from the (market, marked). Every day, Arnie (works, worms) very (hard, harm). He (turms, turns) the soil, which is sometimes called (dirt, diet). When there are lots of (warms, worms) in the soil, it is healthy. There are also lots of animals on the (form, farm). Some are (horns, horses) and others are pigs. Arnie gets (park, pork) from the pigs to sell at the market.

Arnie's *Farm*

ISBN: 978-1-927042-05-2

Predicate of a Sentence

- The **predicate** is the part of the sentence that tells what the subject is doing.

C. Write a predicate for each sentence.

1. In spring, flowers _____

   _____ .

2. In summer, we _____

   _____ .

3. In fall, I _____

   _____ .

4. In winter, I _____

   _____ .

5. My favourite sport _____

   _____ .

6. On Mother's Day, we _____

   _____ .

7. In my dream, I _____

   _____ .

8. My family _____

   _____ .

ISBN: 978-1-927042-05-2

Countries and Languages

D. Fill in the blanks.

Country

Language

Spain	Spanish
Italy	Italian
France	French
Greece	Greek
Canada	English
Romania	Romanian
Hungary	Hungarian

People from many countries in the world, like Canada and the United States, speak 1._____ . In Spain, people speak 2._____ , and in 3._____ , people speak French. In the Eastern European countries of Hungary and Romania, people speak 4._____ and 5._____ . In Italy and Greece, people speak 6._____ and 7._____ .

E. Unscramble these languages.

LIAANTI

1 _____

HASPNSI

2 _____

GRHUAIANN

3 _____

ISBN: 978-1-927042-05-2

Out on the Road

Sign:

A. Time to Nibble
B. Home Sweet Home
C. Time for a Drink
D. Derek Turns the Curve
E. On the Straight and Narrow
F. Derek Hits the Fence

A. Derek the Dog is out on the road. Help him find his way home. Match the story titles with the pictures in the maze. Print the letters in the boxes.

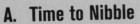

1   2   3

4

5   6

ISBN: 978-1-927042-05-2

Phonics: Diphthongs – ou and ow

- **Diphthongs** are two vowel sounds that make a new sound.

B. Say the words in the clouds below and print them where they belong.

| hound | grow | blow | row | blouse |

| couch | glow | town | brown | rainbow |

| mouse | low | flowers | crown | sound |

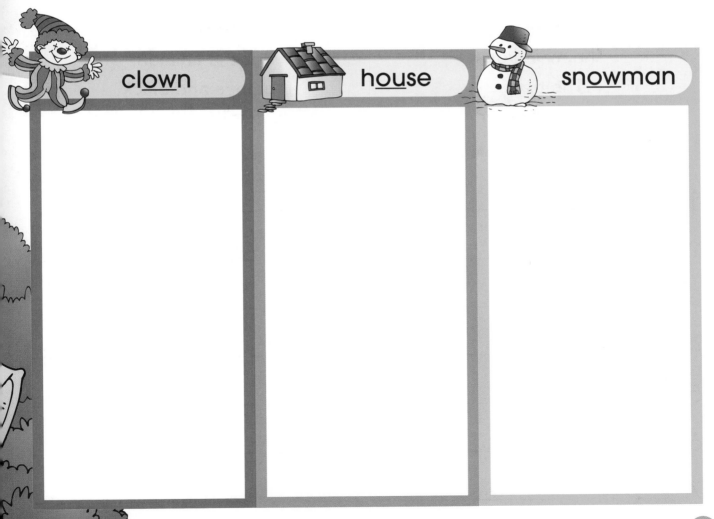

clown   house   snowman

ISBN: 978-1-927042-05-2

Distinguishing Subjects and Predicates

- A sentence has two main parts – a **subject** and a **predicate**.
- The **subject** tells who or what the sentence is about.
- The **predicate** tells what is happening.

C. **Match the subjects with the predicates. Write the sentences on the lines below.**

Subject	Predicate
At the zoo, we	helps clean the cages.
The monkey	has a mane on its neck.
The African elephant	is black and white.
The zebra	likes to hang by its tail.
The male lion	visit the animals.
The tiger	is orange and black.
The zookeeper	is the largest living land animal.

1. _____

2. _____

3. _____

4. _____

5. _____

6. _____

7. _____

ISBN: 978-1-927042-05-2

Homophones

- **Homophones** are words that sound the same but are spelled differently and have different meanings.

D. Match the pictures and words with the homophones.

1. 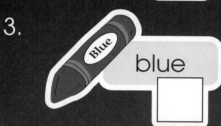 pear

2.  sew

3.  blue

4.  sun

5.  see

6.  toe

7.  flower

8.  witch

A. sea   B. blew   C. flour   D. tow

E. which   F. so   G. pair   H. son

ISBN: 978-1-927042-05-2

The Coin Collection

David has a coin collection. He started it when he was six years old. He has over three hundred coins in his collection.

The first coins he got were three coins from Italy that his mom gave him after a trip there. Since then, many of his family members and friends have given him coins as gifts. He has coins from all over the world.

David's favourite coin is from Sri Lanka. It is large and heavy. Another coin he likes is a Chinese coin with a hole in the centre.

A. Read the story and complete the sentences.

1. David has a _____

2. He has over _____

3. His first coins were _____

4. Many people have given _____

5. He has coins from _____

ISBN: 978-1-927042-05-2

6. David's favourite _____

7. His favourite coin is _____

8. A Chinese coin has _____

Phonics: Diphthongs – oi and oy

- *"Oi" and "oy" sound the same in words, but "oi" is usually found in the middle of a word and "oy" is usually found at the end.*

B. Fill in the blanks with the correct words to complete the sentences.

| coin | toy | annoy | soy | oil |
| boy | joy | boil | point | loyal |

1. Christine has a _____ collection.

2. Marie is a very _____ friend.

3. The _____ likes to play soccer.

4. Ryan gets a lot of _____ from playing sports.

5. The pencil has a very sharp _____ .

6. Some babies drink _____ milk.

7. Don't _____ your brother!

8. Will you _____ the water for tea?

9. The robot is his favourite _____ .

10. _____ is used in cooking.

ISBN: 978-1-927042-05-2

Subject-Verb Agreement

- The **subject** of a sentence must have a **verb** that "**agrees**".

C. **Read the facts about beavers. Choose the verb that agrees with the subject in each sentence.**

1. Beavers _____ members of the aquatic rodent family.   is   are

2. Every beaver _____ a coat of thick coarse fur. have   has

3. Beavers _____ their dams with sticks and mud in streams and small rivers.   build   builds

4. Beavers _____ in colonies, with one or more groups to a lodge.   live   lives

5. A family of beavers _____ of a mother, a father, and two sets of offspring.   consist   consists

6. They _____ in the winter.   breed   breeds

ISBN: 978-1-927042-05-2

Synonyms

- **Synonyms** *are words that mean the same.*

D. Read each sentence below. Circle the word that matches the underlined word.

1. Cindy was <u>weeping</u> when she fell down.

   crying   climbing

2. It was a <u>windy</u> day in the city.

   breezy   cool

3. Mom was <u>exhausted</u> after her trip.

   tired   trying

4. The <u>small</u> child held on to the balloon.

   little   large

5. The weather was <u>humid</u> and warm.

   damp   dry

6. The <u>huge</u> dog ran over to the car.

   big   tiny

7. The kiwi fruit was <u>firm</u> and green.

   hard   soft

8. The Chinese coin has a hole in the <u>centre</u>.

   middle   back

ISBN: 978-1-927042-05-2

1. Turn the oven up to 400° F.

2. Get these ingredients.
   2 cups of flour
   1/2 cup of sugar
   1/2 cup of margarine (melted)
   1/2 tsp of salt
   3 tsp of baking powder
   1 cup of blueberries
   1 egg
   3/4 cup of milk

3. Put all the dry ingredients in a bowl.

4. Put all the wet ingredients in a bowl.

5. Mix the dry ingredients with the wet ingredients.

6. Spoon the mixture into a muffin pan.

7. Bake at 400° F for 15 to 20 minutes.

Making Blueberry Muffins

A. Read the cookbook recipe and circle the correct answers.

1. This recipe is for (muffins, cookies).

2. Milk is a (wet, dry) ingredient.

ISBN: 978-1-927042-05-2

3. The fruit in this recipe is (blackberries, blueberries).

4. The seventh ingredient is (egg, milk).

5. The oven is turned up to (400°F, 400°C).

Phonics: Special Sound – oo

- Words that have "**oo**" in them can sound like "oo" in "room" or "oo" in "cook".

B. Complete the rhymes with the words provided.

cookbook   cook   book   look

My mom taught me to 1._____

By reading a 2._____ .

She said, "Take a 3._____ .

This is called a 4._____ ."

fool   pool   drool

cool

The clown played the 5._____

By jumping in the 6._____ .

He thought it was 7._____

When he started to 8._____ .

ISBN: 978-1-927042-05-2

Word Order: Making Sentences

C. **Put each group of words in order to make a sentence.**

1. start   autumn.   We   in   school

   _____

2. home.   close   My   is   to   school

   _____

3. to   I   from   day.   every   walk   and   school

   _____

4. lunch.   go   I   Sometimes,   home   for

   _____

5. sports   at   There   school.   of   are   lots   my

   _____

6. volleyball.   and   soccer,   play   We   hockey,

   _____

7. muffins   We   soccer.   after   eat   playing

   _____

ISBN: 978-1-927042-05-2

Antonyms

- **Antonyms** are words with opposite meanings.

D. **Read the word inside each kite. Choose the correct antonym from the two words below it.**

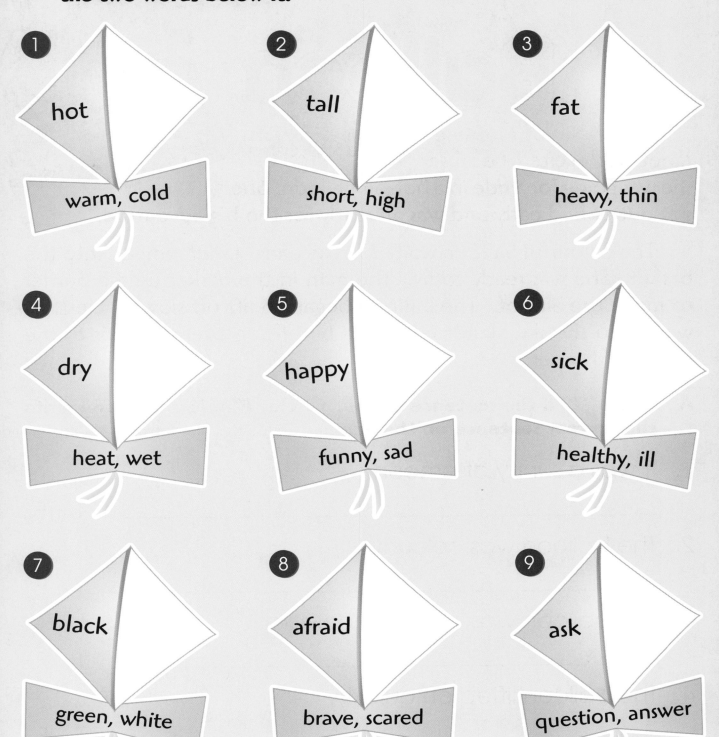

1. hot — warm, cold

2. tall — short, high

3. fat — heavy, thin

4. dry — heat, wet

5. happy — funny, sad

6. sick — healthy, ill

7. black — green, white

8. afraid — brave, scared

9. ask — question, answer

ISBN: 978-1-927042-05-2

A Balloon Ride

It was a sunny morning. Janet was excited because she was going for a ride in a hot-air balloon. She got out of bed early and was all ready for the big adventure.

The colourful balloon waited in the park. Janet jumped into the basket. She was ready to fly. The man in the basket used a burner to make the air hot. The balloon began to lift off slowly. Up they went into the sky. Janet felt like a bird flying over the tops of the trees and houses.

A. Circle "T" if the sentence is true. Circle "F" if it is false and write the correct sentence on the line.

1. It was a sunny afternoon.

   _____ T   F

2. The balloon was colourful.

   _____ T   F

3. The balloon was in the schoolyard.

   _____ T   F

4. The balloon lifted off quickly.

   _____ T   F

ISBN: 978-1-927042-05-2

Phonics: Silent Consonants

- Some words have **silent consonants**. We do not hear the sound of the consonant when we say the word.

  Example: Don't clim<u>b</u> up the tree.

B. Sometimes an "l" is silent. Add the silent "l" and say the words.

① ha ☐ f

② ta ☐ k

③ sta ☐ k

④ wa ☐ k

⑤ ca ☐ f

⑥ pa ☐ m

C. Answer the riddles with the silent "b" words.

(lamb) (limb) (thumb) (crumb)

1. This is a young sheep. _____

2. You should keep this on your plate. _____

3. It is the finger that is nearest your wrist. _____

4. It is another name for a leg. _____

ISBN: 978-1-927042-05-2

Telling (Declarative) Sentences

- A **telling sentence** tells you something.
- It begins with a capital letter and ends with a period (.).
  Example: Bees get nectar from flowers.

D. **Colour the picture and write four sentences about what you see.**

1. _____

   _____

   _____

2. _____

   _____

   _____

3. _____

   _____

   _____

4. _____

   _____

   _____

   _____

HONEY

ISBN: 978-1-927042-05-2

Antonyms

Antonyms are words with opposite meanings.

E. **Find the antonyms in each sentence and write them on the lines below.**

1. The hot-air balloon needs cold air to land.

   _____ _____

2. Janet woke up early so that she would not be late for the balloon ride.

   _____ _____

3. The best time to fly a balloon is on a calm day and the worst time is on a windy day.

   _____ _____   _____ _____

4. Janet opened her eyes when the balloon went up but she closed them when it came down.

   _____ _____   _____ _____

   _____ _____

It isn't really that easy.

F. **Write a sentence using the antonyms "easy" and "hard".**

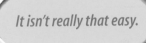

ISBN: 978-1-927042-05-2

Autumn

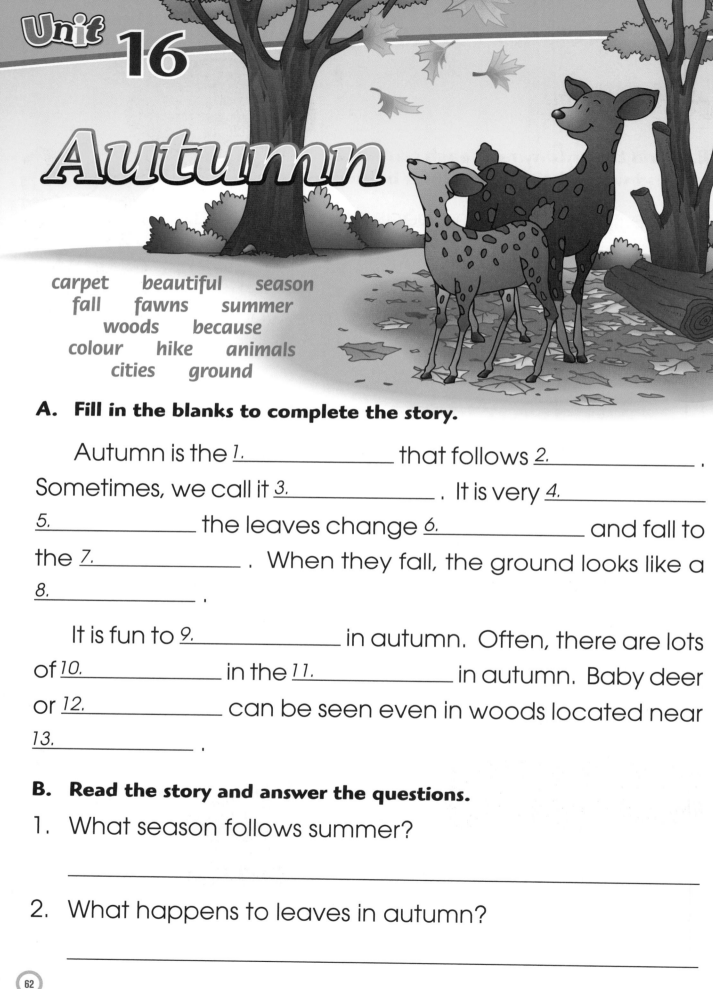

carpet   beautiful   season
fall   fawns   summer
woods   because
colour   hike   animals
cities   ground

A. Fill in the blanks to complete the story.

Autumn is the 1._____ that follows 2._____ .
Sometimes, we call it 3._____ . It is very 4._____
5._____ the leaves change 6._____ and fall to
the 7._____ . When they fall, the ground looks like a
8._____ .

It is fun to 9._____ in autumn. Often, there are lots
of 10._____ in the 11._____ in autumn. Baby deer
or 12._____ can be seen even in woods located near
13._____ .

B. Read the story and answer the questions.

1. What season follows summer?

_____

2. What happens to leaves in autumn?

_____

ISBN: 978-1-927042-05-2

3. Where do you find baby deer in autumn?

   _____

4. What is another name for autumn?

   _____

5. What is fun to do in autumn?

   _____

Phonics: "Sad" Sounds – au and aw

- Both **"au"** and **"aw"** make the **sad sound**. When you say "saw" or "pause" out loud, you can hear why these are sad sounds.

C. Answer the questions with the correct words.

jaw	autumn	yawn	auto
fawn	straw	saw	saucer

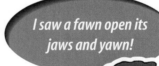

I saw a fawn open its jaws and yawn!

1. What is a baby deer? _____

2. What goes under a cup? _____

3. What is part of your face? _____

4. What do you put in a drink? _____

5. What is another word for car? _____

6. What season is also called fall? _____

7. What can be used to cut wood? _____

8. What do you do when you are sleepy? _____

ISBN: 978-1-927042-05-2

Asking (Interrogative) Sentences

- An **asking sentence** asks a question.
- It begins with a capital letter and ends with a question mark (?).
  Example: What does your spaceship look like?

D. Albert the Alien has just arrived on Earth. If you could ask him five questions, what would they be?

1. _____

   _____

   _____

2. _____

   _____

3. _____

   _____

4. _____

   _____

5. _____

   _____

Ask a friend to pretend that he or she is Albert and answer your questions.

ISBN: 978-1-927042-05-2

Homophones, Synonyms, and Antonyms

E. Read the pair of words on each leaf. Decide whether they are homophones (H), synonyms (S), or antonyms (A). Circle the correct letter.

> Homophones are words that sound the same. Synonyms are words that have similar meanings. Antonyms are words with opposite meanings.

1. breezy windy — H S A

2. pair pear — H S A

3. rise fall — H S A

4. baby adult — H S A

5. sad unhappy — H S A

6. hairy bald — H S A

7. night day — H S A

8. clean tidy — H S A

9. blue blew — H S A

ISBN: 978-1-927042-05-2

Most plants start as a seed. Usually, you plant the seed in the garden or the yard, in shade or sun.

If you use a small trowel, you can dig a hole just big enough to poke the seed down and cover it with more soil.

First, you plant the seed and let the sun shine down on it. After a few weeks, little shoots begin to sprout. Then, the stem gets stronger and leaves begin to show.

All about Plants

A. Read the story and answer the questions.

1. What do most plants start as?

   _____

2. Where do people usually plant seeds?

   _____

3. What do people use to cover a seed?

   _____

4. How long does it take for shoots to sprout?

   _____

ISBN: 978-1-927042-05-2

Phonics: **Words with "y" as a Vowel**

- Sometimes when "**y**" is at the end of a word, it sounds like an "e".
  Examples: many, only, penny

B. Say the words on the left. Match them with the meanings.

funny	another name for rabbit
buddy	causing laughter
carry	bright with sunshine
Mary	friend
bunny	a name for a girl
sunny	take something with you

C. Fill in the missing words.

my   try   why   fly   shy

Sometimes, the "y" at the end of a word sounds like an "i".

1. _____ did she plant the seed there?

2. Did you _____ to ride the bike?

3. We can _____ our kites another day.

4. The child was very _____ .

5. We can go to _____ house to play.

ISBN: 978-1-927042-05-2

Unit 17

Surprising (Exclamatory) Sentences

- *Wow! A **surprising sentence** is a sentence that shows strong feeling.*
- *It begins with a capital letter and ends with an exclamation mark (!).*

D. Read the sentences. What would you say in each case? Write the exclamations.

1. You found a $10 bill on the ground.

_____

2. You learned to ride a two-wheeler.

_____

3. You have just read your first book.

_____

4. You just learned to swim.

_____

5. You have a new puppy.

_____

6. You won the first prize.

_____

7. You are going to Disney World.

_____

ISBN: 978-1-927042-05-2

Months of the Year

E. Read the sentences below. Fill in the correct months.

October   July   January   June
November   April   December   February
March   May   August   September

1.   In _____ , it is Christmas.

2.   School starts in _____ .

3.   Valentine's Day falls in _____ .

4.   Halloween is at the end of _____ .

5.   The first month of the year is _____ .

6.   School ends for the summer vacation in _____ .

7.   The eighth month of the year is _____ .

8.   The fourth month of the year is _____ .

9.   St. Patrick's Day is in _____ .

10.   Victoria Day is in _____ .

11.   Canada Day is in _____ .

12.   Remembrance Day is in _____ .

ISBN: 978-1-927042-05-2

Penguins

Penguins are birds that cannot fly but are good swimmers. They live in Antarctica and off the coasts of Africa and Australia. The smallest penguin is 40 centimetres tall. It is called the Blue Fairy. The tallest penguin is the Emperor. It can be up to 120 cm tall.

Penguins feed on fish, squid, and small shrimp. They are the prey of leopard seals and killer whales. The female penguin lays an egg or two and goes off in search of food. While she is gone, the male hatches the eggs on his feet under a layer of fur.

A. Read the story and fill in the blanks.

1. Penguins live in _____ and off the coasts of _____ and _____ .

2. The smallest penguin is called the _____ .

3. It is 40 _____ tall.

4. The tallest penguin is called the _____ .

5. Penguins feed on _____ , _____ , and _____ .

6. The _____ lays eggs and the _____ hatches them.

ISBN: 978-1-927042-05-2

Phonics: **Soft and Hard "c" and "g"**

- The letters "**c**" and "**g**" have both **soft** and **hard sounds**.
  Examples: celery (soft "c" sound); can (hard "c" sound)
           ginger (soft "g" sound); go (hard "g" sound)

B. **Read the words and place them in the correct ice floes below.**

ISBN: 978-1-927042-05-2

Imperative (Command) Sentences

• A **command** is a sentence that tells someone to do something.

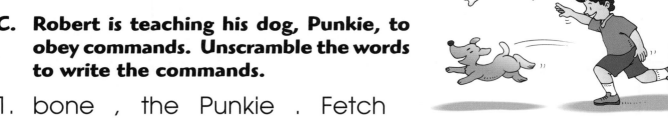

C. Robert is teaching his dog, Punkie, to obey commands. Unscramble the words to write the commands.

1. bone , the Punkie . Fetch

   _____

   _____

2. newspaper . and Punkie , get the go

   _____

   _____

3. shoe . Find Punkie , the

   _____

   _____

4. mouth . leash Take in the your

   _____

   _____

5. toy . the Find

   _____

   _____

6. chase Don't the car .

   _____

   _____

ISBN: 978-1-927042-05-2

We use computers everywhere – at school, at home, at the doctor's, the dentist's, and department stores. It is important to know the main parts of the computer. The <u>monitor</u> is the screen that displays words and pictures. When you type on a <u>keyboard</u>, your words appear on the monitor. If you want a paper copy, you can use a <u>printer</u> to print the words or pictures. To save work from your computer, you can use a flash <u>drive</u>, or CDs, which look like the ones you use to play music. If you add a <u>modem</u> to your computer, you can communicate with other people.

Word Search

D. Circle the words that are underlined above.

z	b	y	d	i	m	k	d	r	i	v	e
o	u	n	o	q	c	k	b	s	j	x	c
j	p	r	i	n	t	e	r	a	l	b	o
k	d	b	i	a	b	y	o	f	e	u	m
o	e	a	u	e	u	b	h	c	j	i	p
r	u	f	c	r	m	o	d	e	m	b	u
i	c	t	d	s	c	a	o	n	e	r	t
m	o	n	i	t	o	r	d	k	e	l	e
j	v	s	i	w	o	d	h	g	s	k	r

ISBN: 978-1-927042-05-2

ISBN: 978-1-927042-05-2

Answers

1 The Bumblebee

A. 1. It is an insect.
   2. It is yellow and black.
   3. The queen bee is the leader.
   4. She lays eggs after a winter in hibernation.

B. 1. leaf   2. cap
   3. bat   4. jug
   5. yarn   6. wagon
   7. goat   8. rabbit
   9. duck   10. top
   11. fan   12. queen
   13. sun   14. hat

C. 1. bees   2. dogs
   3. insects   4. desks
   5. ships   6. tables
   7. bears   8. girls
   9. rulers   10. lakes
   11. boats   12. roads
   13. toys   14. trees
   15. flowers   16. plants
   17. rugs   18. flags
   19. boys   20. masks

D. 1. A square is a shape with four equal sides.
   2. A triangle is a shape with three sides.
   3. A circle is a single line.
   4. A rectangle is a shape with opposite sides that are equal.

2 The Museum Trip

A. 1. B   2. B
   3. B   4. C

B. 1. bus   2. box
   3. nest   4. dime
   5. tulip   6. mask
   7. bar   8. pot
   9. pen   10. bone
   11. can   12. ball
   13. sock   14. saw
   15. kite   16. rake

C. 1. ROM
   2. Ontario
   3. Venus
   4. Mrs. Smith
   5. Mark
   6. Punkie
   7. Portland Drive
   8. Mars

9. Canada Day
10. Sunday
11. Ottawa
12. Charlotte's Web
13. Deer Lake
14. May

D. 1. Hockey   2. Baseball
   3. Hockey ; Baseball 4. Hockey
   5. Baseball   6. Hockey
   7. Baseball   8. Hockey ; Baseball

3 The Channel Tunnel

A. 1. It links England and France.
   2. It was built in 1993.
   3. Napoleon was the French emperor in 1802.
   4. Two tunnels are for trains to carry people and one is for emergency and service.

B. 1. lamp   2. web
   3. mop   4. jug
   5. pot   6. bag
   7. desk   8. bell
   9. net   10. can
   11. lips   12. fan
   13. tent   14. rock
   15. six   16. nut

C.   six street lights ; four cars
      ten flowers ; two boys
      five bicycles ; seven trees
      nine parking meters ; three trucks

D. 1. cup ; bowl ; glass
   2. blackboard ; desk ; eraser
   3. tires ; horn ; key
   4. swing ; seesaw ; slide
   5. pear ; grapes ; apple

4 Snakes

A. 1. reptiles   2. long
   3. cold   4. eggs
   5. laid   6. hibernation
   7. skins   8. move
   9. place

B. 1. bike   2. hive
   3. pole   4. cone
   5. cake   6. tube
   7. kite   8. ruler
   9. gate   10. tulip

ISBN: 978-1-927042-05-2

Answers

C.   (Individual writing)

D. 1. recipe
   2. cupboard/box
   3. ingredients
   4. cupboard
   5. refrigerator
   6. pot ; stove ; melted
   7. square

5   What Happens Next?

A.   (Individual writing)

B. 1. snail   2. day
   3. nail   4. jay
   5. tray   6. paint
   7. tail   8. pay
   9. say   10. play

C. 1. is   2. are
   3. is   4. is
   5. are   6. are
   7. are   8. am
   9. is   10. is

D.

q	w	f	s	w	h	o	f	x	f	h	k	t
h	b	k	n	e	b	k	r	b	h	l	g	r
r	o	x	a	l	m	n	o	k	l	w	z	a
p	k	f	i	q	a	g	z	l	z	s	n	i
q	g	c	l	a	y	o	c	z	n	a	i	l
r	o	e	q	c	d	k	d	r	f	y	j	h
b	h	q	t	e	l	f	e	s	w	e	h	f
q	x	o	r	v	b	p	r	a	y	r	l	n
z	d	r	a	f	w	f	w	d	n	p	q	l
p	l	a	y	w	o	x	o	r	s	t	i	s
s	t	x	x	h	e	d	x	h	x	a	x	h
g	d	h	b	o	l	k	b	c	h	r	i	m
r	a	o	f	r	b	s	l	e	t	s	g	l
h	y	m	l	x	m	l	b	x	n	a	y	b

6   Days of the Week

A.   (Suggested answers)
   2. will go to the beach.
   3. he will ride on the roller coaster.
   4. he will go to the library.
   5. he will paint a picture.
   6. he will go to the children's playground.
   7. (Individual drawing and writing)

B. 1. week   2. jeans
   3. tea   4. team
   5. bean   6. meat
   7. weed   8. bee
   9. sea   10. seed

C.

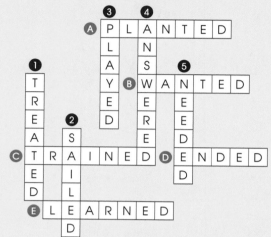

D.   Months of the Year:
      January ; February ; March ; April ; May ; June ;
      July ; August ; September ; October ; November ;
      December
      Days of the Week:
      Sunday ; Monday ; Tuesday ; Wednesday ;
      Thursday ; Friday ; Saturday

7   The CN Tower

A. 1. self-supporting towers in the world.
   2. five and a half football fields.
   3. as deep as a five-storey building.
   4. improve the broadcasting of radio and television
      signals.
   5. a person hopping down its 1899 steps on a pogo stick.

B. 1. clear   2. clowns
   3. slide   4. black
   5. glass   6. sled
   7. flag   8. blew
   9. plate   10. glad
  11. clock   12. play

C. 1. build   thought
   2. drink   built
   3. ring   drank
   4. think   left
   5. drive   drove
   6. leave   rang

ISBN: 978-1-927042-05-2

D. 1. eat 2. go
3. break 4. swim
5. lose 6. make

E. (Suggested drawings)

1.  triangle	2. quadrilateral
3. hexagon	4. heptagon
5. pentagon	6. octagon

8 Sir John A. Macdonald

A. 1. Sir John A. Macdonald was the first prime minister of Canada.
2. He was born in Glasgow, Scotland.
3. He was five years old when he came to Ontario.
4. The Dominion of Canada was formed in 1867.
5. He was best known for the completion of the Pacific Railway.

B. (Suggested answers)
prune ; prime ; crop
broom ; grape ; bring
cream ; fruit ; braid
grass ; drone ; prize
trap ; tree ; frog
drum ; dress ; truck
crab ; trail ; true
grip ; breed ; frame
green ; crime ; cross
free ; frail ; groom

C. 1. The <u>tired</u> boys rested under the <u>shady</u> tree.
2. He put a <u>big</u> book into a <u>small</u> bag.
3. The <u>friendly</u> nurse is helping the <u>sick</u> girl.
4. The <u>old</u> man is talking to the <u>young</u> child.
5. She picked a <u>red</u> apple from the <u>tall</u> tree.
6. The <u>prime</u> minister was a <u>great</u> man.

D. (Individual writing)

E. 1. first
2. eighth
3. second
4. sixth
5. fifth
6. fourth
7. seventh
8. ninth
9. third
10. tenth

9 Dance Lessons

A. 1. ballet
2. slippers
3. day
4. ten
5. many
6. good
7. dance
8. costumes
9. fun
10. hip-hop

B. 1. started
2. space
3. stairs
4. stove
5. skunk
6. snake
7. snack
8. swim
9. skip
10. small
11. swat
12. snip
13. snap
14. spoon

C. 1. Polar bears live in the Arctic. They are big and white. <u>Big paws.</u> They have small eyes and ears. <u>Jump from ice floe to ice floe.</u>
2. Polar bears have other names. <u>Sometimes called white bears, sea bears, or ice bears.</u> <u>Swim very well.</u>
3. Polar bears move fast and travel far. <u>Eat seals and fish.</u> The male is usually larger than the female. <u>Hairy feet.</u>
4. Baby bears or cubs are born in winter. <u>Weigh less than one kilogram when born.</u> <u>Remain with mothers from ten months to two years.</u>

ISBN: 978-1-927042-05-2

Answers

D. 1. penny
2. toonie
3. dime
4. quarter
5. loonie
6. nickel

10 The Treasure Chest

A. (Suggested answers)
1. Rob heard about a sunken ship in Sharaz.
2. They decided to search for the sunken treasure.

B. 1. Ch ; ch ; ch ; ch   2. Sh ; sh ; sh
3. Th ; th ; th ; th ; th
4. wh ; wh ; wh ; wh ; wh ; wh ; wh

C. 1. ship   2. chest
3. whiskers   4. thick
5. peach   6. moth

D. 1. The chest   2. Apples
3. The Earth   4. A computer
5. Skating   6. The time
7. (Individual drawing and answer)

E. 1. horse   2. cow
3. rabbit   4. dog
5. kangaroo   6. pig
7. chicken   8. goose
9. cat   10. deer

11 A Visit to the Farm

A. 1. There are different kinds of farms.
2. They visited a dairy farm.
3. He used big machines to milk the cows.

B. Arnie's <u>farm</u> is <u>far</u> from the <u>market</u>. Every day, Arnie <u>works</u> very <u>hard</u>. He <u>turns</u> the soil, which is sometimes called <u>dirt</u>. When there are lots of <u>worms</u> in the soil, it is healthy. There are also lots of animals on the <u>farm</u>. Some are <u>horses</u> and others are pigs. Arnie gets <u>pork</u> from the pigs to sell at the market.

C. (Individual writing)

D. 1. English
2. Spanish
3. France
4. Hungarian
5. Romanian
6. Italian
7. Greek

E. 1. ITALIAN   2. SPANISH   3. HUNGARIAN

12 Out on the Road

A. 1. A   2. F
3. E   4. D
5. C   6. B

B. clown: town ; brown ; flowers ; crown
house: hound ; blouse ; couch ; mouse ; sound
snowman: grow ; blow ; row ; glow ; rainbow ; low

C. (Order may vary.)
1. At the zoo, we visit the animals.
2. The monkey likes to hang by its tail.
3. The African elephant is the largest living land animal.
4. The zebra is black and white.
5. The male lion has a mane on its neck.
6. The tiger is orange and black.
7. The zookeeper helps clean the cages.

D. 1. G   2. F
3. B   4. H
5. A   6. D
7. C   8. E

13 The Coin Collection

A. 1. coin collection.
2. three hundred coins.
3. from Italy.
4. him coins as gifts.
5. all over the world.
6. coin is from Sri Lanka.
7. large and heavy.
8. a hole in the centre.

B. 1. coin   2. loyal
3. boy   4. joy
5. point   6. soy
7. annoy   8. boil
9. toy   10. Oil

C. 1. are   2. has
3. build   4. live
5. consists   6. breed

D. 1. crying   2. breezy
3. tired   4. little
5. damp   6. big
7. hard   8. middle

14 Making Blueberry Muffins

A. 1. muffins   2. wet
3. blueberries   4. egg
5. 400°F

ISBN: 978-1-927042-05-2

B. 1. cook   2. book
   3. look   4. cookbook
   5. fool   6. pool
   7. cool   8. drool

C. 1. We start school in autumn.
   2. My school is close to home.
   3. I walk to and from school every day.
   4. Sometimes, I go home for lunch.
   5. There are lots of sports at my school.
   6. We play hockey, soccer, and volleyball./
      We play soccer, hockey, and volleyball.
   7. We eat muffins after playing soccer.

D. 1. cold   2. short
   3. thin   4. wet
   5. sad   6. healthy
   7. white   8. brave
   9. answer

15   A Balloon Ride

A. 1. It was a sunny morning. ; F
   2. T
   3. The balloon was in the park. ; F
   4. The balloon lifted off slowly. ; F

B. 1. half   2. talk
   3. stalk   4. walk
   5. calf   6. palm

C. 1. lamb
   2. crumb
   3. thumb
   4. limb

D. (Individual colouring and writing)

E. 1. hot ; cold
   2. early ; late
   3. best ; worst ;
     calm ; windy
   4. opened ; closed ;
     went ; came ;
     up ; down

F. (Individual writing)

16   Autumn

A. 1. season
   2. summer
   3. fall
   4. beautiful
   5. because
   6. colour

   7. ground
   8. carpet
   9. hike
  10. animals
  11. woods
  12. fawns
  13. cities

B. 1. Autumn follows summer.
   2. They change colour and fall to the ground.
   3. We find them in woods located near cities.
   4. Another name for autumn is fall.
   5. It is fun to hike in autumn.

C. 1. fawn   2. saucer
   3. jaw   4. straw
   5. auto   6. autumn
   7. saw   8. yawn

D. (Individual writing)

E. 1. S   2. H
   3. A   4. A
   5. S   6. A
   7. A   8. S
   9. H

17   All about Plants

A. 1. They start as a seed.
   2. They usually plant them in the garden or the yard.
   3. They cover it with soil.
   4. It takes a few weeks for shoots to sprout.

B.

funny	another name for rabbit
buddy	causing laughter
carry	bright with sunshine
Mary	friend
bunny	a name for a girl
sunny	take something with you

C. 1. Why   2. try
   3. fly   4. shy
   5. my

D. (Individual writing)

E. 1. December
   2. September
   3. February
   4. October
   5. January

ISBN: 978-1-927042-05-2

6. June
7. August
8. April
9. March
10. May
11. July
12. November

18 Penguins

A. 1. Antarctica ; Africa ; Australia
2. Blue Fairy
3. centimetres
4. Emperor
5. fish ; squid ; shrimp
6. female ; male

B. SOFT c: city ; civil ; cent
HARD c: carrot ; cake ; cub ; cook
SOFT g: giant ; gym ; gem ; giraffe
HARD g: gate ; gift ; goose ; girl

C. 1. Fetch the bone, Punkie.
2. Punkie, go and get the newspaper.
3. Find the shoe, Punkie.
4. Take the leash in your mouth.
5. Find the toy.
6. Don't chase the car.

E.

z	b	y	d	i	m	k	d	r	i	v	e
o	u	n	o	q	c	k	b	s	j	x	c
j	p	r	i	n	t	e	r	a	l	b	o
k	d	b	i	a	b	y	o	f	e	u	m
o	e	a	u	e	u	b	h	c	j	i	p
r	u	f	c	r	m	o	d	e	m	b	u
i	c	t	d	s	c	a	o	n	e	r	t
m	o	n	i	t	o	r	d	k	e	l	e
j	v	s	i	w	o	d	h	g	s	k	r

ISBN: 978-1-927042-05-2